the saga of
alexander the great

sofia zarabouka

ISBN 960-04-1336-3

Title in Greek: Σοφία Ζαραμπούκα «Ο Μεγαλέξανδρος»

the saga of alexander the great

sofia zarabouka

Translation
ALKISTIS DIMAS

kedros

PROLOGUE

*In 356 B.C. Alexander the Great, son of King
Philip, was born in the northern Greek city of
Aeges in Macedonia. At that time, the mainland
of Greece and the islands were divided into
small states. Greek city-states also spread from
the Black Sea to every shore of the
Mediterranean.*
*Each state had its own leader and although they
all spoke the same language and considered
themselves Greeks, it was not uncommon for
them to fight among themselves. King Philip
proved to be the strongest of the leaders and set
about organising all the Greeks against the
Persians.*
*In the spring of 334 B.C., the sudden death of
Philip brought Alexander to the Macedonian
throne. At the age of only twenty-two,
Alexander the Great found himself the leader of
30,000 foot-soldiers and 5000 cavalry. He was
exceptionally brave and well educated and had a
passion for advancing the Greek nation.
Immediately he went ahead with the great
expedition against the king of Persia, Darius. In
a series of battles, the Persians were defeated.
After the death of Darius, Alexander was
expected to return to Greece. But as well as
being a conqueror, he also had a strong sense of
adventure and decided to continue eastwards –*

through present-day Turkey into Syria, Iraq, Iran, Afghanistan, Pakistan and finally, back westwards to Egypt. Along the way he founded cities which bore his name – Alexandria in Egypt being the most famous.

In the spring of 323 B.C., at the age of almost thirty-three, Alexander died of fever in the city of Babylon. It had taken him only a little more than ten years to create an empire of one and a half million square miles. He himself had covered 25,000 miles in three continents. He was one of the greatest generals of all time, a brilliant tactician, who never lost a battle, and an excellent student of human character. He explored far beyond the geographical boundaries known at that time and discovered new territories. He charted new trade routes and made Greek the common language for the world he conquered. Last but not least: in changing the world, he changed himself with it.

According to Greek tradition, in the course of
great storms when the sky is full of dark clouds and
the waves grow as high as mountains, a mermaid
springs out of the waters, seizes the first ship she
encounters and makes it stop.
"Is King Alexander alive and well?" she asks in a
fierce tone of voice. Then the person facing her
must find the courage to answer:
"He's alive and well and he rules the world!"
At once the waters become calm and the mermaid,
who happens to be the favourite sister of
Alexander the Great, allows the ship to continue
its voyage.
Whoever dares to tell her the truth – namely that
Alexander the Great has been dead for over 2000
years – cannot escape her wrath. The mermaid lifts
the boat and dashes it deep into the dark waters.
The sea swallows it up and it is lost for ever.

There are many stories about Alexander.
Some are real and others are legend. In actual fact,
so many centuries have passed since his death;
and yet, unlike other conquerors, people still
remember him. So there must have been

something good and worth loving in him, because
otherwise they would not go on talking about him.

He is remembered not only in Greece,
where he was born, but in all the places where he
ruled. Perhaps because he respected the people he
conquered and wanted to learn their customs.
In some cases, he even emulated them.
He dressed the way they did, tasted the food they
ate, participated in their festive celebrations and
listened attentively to their viewpoints.
He tried to understand their way of life, instead
of forcing his own life-style on them.
This is why the stories and legends of all the
peoples he conquered present him in local
dress and familiar with customs totally unknown in
his birthplace.

A few years ago in Vergina, which is an ancient
site near the city of Salonica, archaeologists
discovered the tomb of Alexander's father, Philip.
On a mound near the ruins of an old palace,
they excavated carefully until they uncovered a
royal tomb. It had been there all these centuries,
although no one knew anything about it.
A gold chest was found containing Philip's bones
wrapped in a piece of purple material and crowned
by a gold wreath. Nearby, the archaeologists also
discovered the king's armour along with various
personal objects. Thus we know that King Philip
lived and died in Macedonia.

Alexander the Great, son of Philip,
was born there too.
His mother was the daughter of the king of Epirus
and her name was Olympia.

The young prince was not allowed any pampering
by his parents. They did not want to spoil him,
so they demanded that his teachers be strict.

Most of his time was devoted to exercising and
learning the use of weapons. Young Alexander
was fearless.

There is a story about a black stallion that one day
started running wildly through the courtyard.
Five trainers chased it, but were unable to mount it.
All of a sudden the horse stopped short.
Not a soul dared to approach except young
Alexander, who moved swiftly, mounted and
mastered the steed. Henceforth the proud horse
belonged to Alexander and was called Bucephalus,
which means "The-One-with-the-Head-of-an-Ox".

When Alexander became a teenager, his father
asked the famous philosopher Aristotle to tutor
the prince in politics, philosophy, poetry and
drama.

Throughout Philip's reign the main enemy of the
Greek city-states were the Persians.
While the Greeks were at war among themselves,
the Persians were busy defeating the Greek cities
in Asia Minor.
The Athenians, who were the traditional leaders
of the other city-states, did not approve
of Philip's gaining power in the North.
So they decided to fight him at Chaeronia.
Alexander took part in that battle, displaying great
courage. The Athenians suffered a bitter loss.
Most of their men were killed.
Alexander's father demanded that the young
prince escort the ashes of the dead Athenians back
to their city to be buried there.
Alexander was delighted to agree, because he was
an admirer of Athenian culture.

After this battle Philip was accepted by everybody – except the Spartans – as Commander-in-Chief of the Greeks against the Persian threat.
Each city-state was free and independent, but was required to supply Philip with soldiers and weapons.

By the summer of 336 B.C. everything was ready for the expedition to Asia. Before his departure, Philip organised games and festivities to celebrate his daughter's marriage. Accompanied by his court, he entered the theatre to attend a performance given specially for the occasion. Suddenly a young man rushed on him out of the crowd and stabbed him to death.
That was the end of Philip.

At the age of only twenty, Alexander was obliged to take his father's place. His first act was to gather around him all his childhood friends: Hephaestion, Crateros, Seleucus, Ptolemy and Perdicca. These men took charge of the infantry and cavalry.

And so the expedition to Asia began. In addition to the Macedonian army, Alexander was in command of 7000 foot-soldiers from various city-states and 1800 horsemen from Thessaly.
There were also the camp followers.
Furthermore, his entourage included botanists, geographers and even historians who recorded the details of how the expedition was progressing.

After crossing the Hellespont, Alexander reached the shores of Asia Minor. When he set foot on land he seized a spear and stuck it in the ground. "This land is ours!" he exclaimed.

King Darius of Persia, who was known as the King of Kings and whose kingdom was truly vast, paid no attention at all to this bold young man. Confident of his own power, he let Alexander advance.

Darius' empire spread all the way from Egypt to the Indus River and embraced deserts, mountains, fertile valleys and big rivers.
Many different peoples lived under Persian rule. They were free to speak their own languages and worship their own gods. But each tribe was governed by one of the noble Persian families devoted to Darius.
His army, though, was not at all in good shape. Many of his soldiers had gotten used to a luxurious way of life and had become lazy and lackadaisical.

Alexander, on the contrary, was full of vim and vigour. He believed his ancestors went back to Achilles and Hercules. He was reared on the *Iliad* and the *Odyssey*. That's why the very first thing he did in Asia Minor was to visit Troy. When he found Achilles' grave, he placed a wreath upon it.

In May of 334 B.C., the Persian generals decided
that Alexander was going too far and should be
given a lesson. So they gathered their cavalry
along the banks of the Granicus River.
They were millions of them.
But Alexander was quite undaunted and led his
men into battle, spreading panic in the hearts of
the Persians. He was present on all fronts, astride
his black steed Bucephalus.
At many points his life was in danger, since
everyone had their eyes on him and he was
the target of every general of the enemy. Finally,
the Persians were forced to beat a hasty retreat.

Following his victory, Alexander marched on to
Sardes, a flourishing city of Asia Minor. There he
acted cleverly. Instead of dismissing the local
rulers, he let them stay on and keep their
privileges. At the same time he appointed a Greek
overseer. Thus his enemies had no choice but to
collaborate with him.

Summer was over now and Alexander decided to
spend the winter in Gordium at the far tip of Asia
Minor. As soon as he arrived there, he was told
about the prophecy concerning the Gordian knot.
According to the oracle, whoever managed to
undo the intricate knot on the pole of a particular
chariot was destined to become master of Asia.
Alexander asked to be taken to the chariot
at once. But when he saw the knot, he realised
it was impossible to undo it. So he wielded his
sword with an energetic thrust and cut the knot
in two. "There now!" said he, "I have undone the
Gordian knot!"

With the spring of 333 B.C., the armies of Alexander moved on again until they reached the renowned Persian port of Tarsus.

This time Darius, King of Kings, was really alarmed. He made up his mind to organise the royal army in order to get rid of Alexander once and for all. He mustered men from all parts of his empire. Innumerable foot-soldiers and horsemen from all the various tribes gathered near Babylon. It was difficult to mobilise such a throng. Darius and the upper echelons of his army brought their families along, all of whom had an entourage of servants and slaves, plus carriages stuffed with furniture and silks and precious jewels. Along the way, wherever they halted, they pitched luxurious tents decorated with rich carpets. This was hardly the way to wage a war!

For the site of the coming battle, Darius chose Issus. But the narrow plain made it hard for his troops to move and the Persians were crushed. It was sheer havoc. Panic-stricken, Darius was compelled to watch, as his soldiers fell in successive waves. In despair he fled, leaving behind him his own family and heaps of spoils. Alexander behaved kindly to Darius' wife, children and mother, when they were brought to him. He told them that henceforth, they must honour him as the master of Asia.

At this point, the Greek army took to the road along the seacoast and conquered two other important cities. The third city, Tyre, managed to hold out against their attack, for it was like an island. In the port Alexander constructed a wharf made of stones and gravel and dirt enabling his soldiers to approach, while his fleet surrounded Tyre from the sea.

The people of Tyre did their best. They hurled
rocks and aimed flaming arrows at the Greek fleet.
But there was no way to win and the siege dragged
on and on. From the islands of Rhodes and Cyprus,
more ships were added to the Greek fleet.
Tyre was unable to hold out any longer and
surrendered.
Now, Alexander's power was
acknowledged by one and all, not only on land,
but also on the high seas.

After appointing Parmenion, one of his childhood
friends, as ruler of the city, Alexander decided to
march on to Egypt. It took him and his men seven
days to cross the desert. His fleet had arrived and
was waiting at the mouth of the Nile.
Without even putting up a fight,
Memphis – the capital of Egypt – surrendered.
The Greeks, and there were many of them in the
cities of Egypt, gave Alexander an enthusiastic
welcome as their liberator.
Alexander respected the Egyptian gods and
ordered sacrifices to them. This made a very
favourable impression on the high priests of
Egypt, who bestowed on him the title
of Pharaoh and other royal titles. After they had
set the regal Egyptian crown on his head,
everyone considered the kingdom of Egypt to
have been united with Macedonia.
Alexander intended to build a new city there and
give it his name. Before starting out, he decided to
visit the famous oracle of Ammon and ask where
the new city should be built along the Nile.
To reach the oracle, he and a few of his
companions had to cross a desert. Local guides
preceded and marked the way on the sand.
Suddenly the wind began to blow. All the marks
they had left along the way were wiped out.
Alexander and his men could only see
mounds of sand.

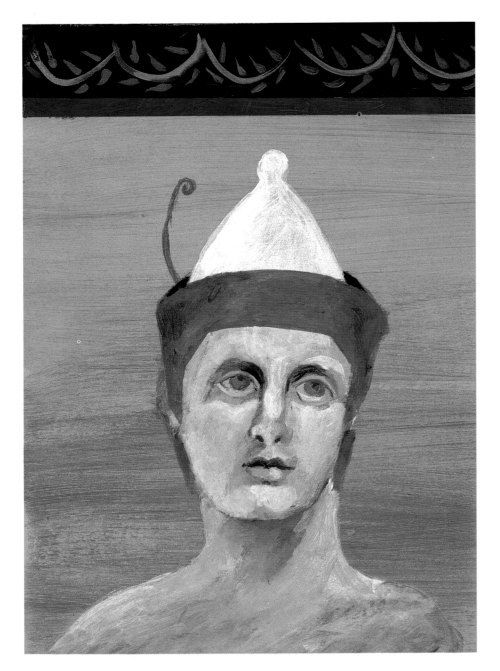

The group had no idea which way to go and they
became desperate. Just then, two snakes appeared
out of the blue. Speaking with a human voice, they
bade the men to follow them.
These snakes had been sent by the Egyptian god
Ammon to show them the way to his temple.
The miracle was interpreted as a sign that the
Egyptian god was on Alexander's side.
So when he finally reached the temple,
Ammon's prophet told the young king that his fate
was to conquer the world.
He also showed Alexander precisely

where to build the city, which would bear
his name – Alexandria.

Meanwhile, the Persian king Darius was
organising a new army with soldiers enlisted from
all over his empire.
There were 200,000 foot-soldiers
and 45,000 cavalry, 200 chariots and masses
of elephants, waiting for the Greeks at Gaugamela.
As soon as Alexander heard about all this,
he hastened to mobilise his own army.
He built two bridges, crossing first the Euphrates
and then the Tigris Rivers. One morning his troops
found themselves face to face with
the Persian army.
This was to be the most large-scale battle of all.
The Persians were soon annihilated by the skilful
movements of the Greeks. And Darius, as usual,
fled for his life.

Instead of pursuing him, Alexander and his men
headed for Babylon. This beautiful city,
full of all the riches and palaces of Darius,
offered no resistance.
As was his habit, he made sacrifices to the local
gods of the city. This had a soothing effect
on the local people who no longer looked upon
him as a foreign conqueror.
Alexander entered in triumph.
The people showered flower-petals on him
and the elders gave him precious gifts.
The Persian guardian of the palace-treasures
handed over the keys.
Alexander appointed two of Darius'
administrators to high positions and his trust in
them persuaded them to consider him their new
master.

Now all roads led to Susa, the actual capital of the Persian empire. He and his men were welcomed as warmly as in Babylon. Alexander was offered camels and Indian elephants.

In the city of Susa the great kings of Persia used to store their treasures, all of which belonged to Alexander now: mounds of gold, silver, precious stones.

It was at this time that coins with the head of Alexander were minted and circulated widely. There must have been a great many of these coins, because we can still find them either deep in the ground or for sale in antique shops.

Every so often Alexander mobilised more infantry and cavalry from Macedonia and other Greek mercenaries. On the other hand, he sent married or sick soldiers back home. After renewing his army with vigorous men, he was ready to move on to another great city – Persepolis.

On the way, they were several times attacked by bands of Persians who tried to stop them. The soldiers were in a nasty mood and when they entered this city of splendid rich palaces, they started plundering. They killed all the men and made slaves of the women.

More treasures accumulated for Alexander. To transport them, he needed 10,000 pairs of mules and 5000 camels.

The local people disapproved when Alexander went up to the acropolis and then, on to the royal palace, as if he were the King of Kings himself. That same night, after a drunken revel, Alexander's soldiers were permitted to burn the palace. This was not Alexander's usual way of doing things and at a later point, he tried to make excuses for it. He claimed it was intended as a punishment of the Persians for the disaster their king Xerxes had caused the city of Athens 150 years earlier.

After his defeat at Gaugamela, Darius went to Ecbatana, the city where his summer palace was situated. He was still extremely wealthy and in a position to organise a new army. But when he was told that Alexander was still pursuing him, he retreated yet again with as much of his army and wealth as he could rescue.

Along the way he and his generals had to abandon their supplies and families. Here and there, groups of his soldiers remained behind, waiting for the chance to join Alexander's army.

Darius' closest companions had lost their confidence in him as a leader,
so they decided to murder him.

They imagined this act would please Alexander, but they were wrong.

He punished the murderers and ordered a royal funeral in honour of Darius.

Alexander's aim was to make the Persian elite accept him as the rightful heir to the throne.
He needed their cooperation. Most of his Greek soldiers had returned home or were tired and unwilling to carry on. With Darius' death, they thought they had fulfilled the purpose of their expedition. But not so Alexander. He did *not* want to go back: there was more of the world to discover and conquer. He longed to move on to the far reaches of the Orient.

He summoned his men and spoke to them with enthusiasm. As he was a very persuasive orator, they agreed to follow him once again.

They set out for what is known today as Afghanistan. But the Greeks, even his own generals, were worn out and the disputes increased. His friend, Philotas, worked up the courage to state in public what all the others were saying in private – though nobody dared to say it straight to Alexander's face.

Philotas said that Alexander was acting like a
Persian monarch, following the customs of the
Persian court, wearing Persian garments and even
the crown of the King of Kings. Apparently he
preferred the company of the Persian lords and
enjoyed listening to their advice. All this was
perfectly obvious, but Alexander was furious and
ordered that Philotas be put to death.

Now the soldiers had to climb the Indian side of
the Caucasus, with the city of Bactra as their
destination. But along the way, there were
enormous difficulties. There wasn't enough food to

go round and the mountain paths were rough and inaccessible.

The Macedonian generals were very worried as they watched Alexander continuing to change more and more, before their very eyes.
He completely forgot the customs of his motherland and turned into a genuine Persian despot.
Alexander ignored his friends' anxiety.
He was absolutely indifferent to their fears and out of spite, he married a lovely local princess by the name of Roxane. Nevertheless the wedding was celebrated just as in his native land.
According to the customs of Macedonia,

the bridegroom meets the bride with a loaf of
bread in his hands and then he uses his sword to cut
the bread in two for the couple to share.
He also advised his soliders to marry local women
and to beget children, with whom they would play
and talk and to feel nostalgia for Greece.

By now his army had thinned out.
In every city he conquered, he left Greek
garrisons.
He reorganised his men and recruited local
soldiers. So when the time came to set out for
India, he was at the head of an army which was no
longer Greek.

Before this new adventure, he tried to find out as
much as possible about the people of India.
He met local dignitaries and adopted their style
of dress. He wanted them to consider him one
of themselves, because he needed their support.
He learned as much as he could about the local
disputes and conflicts in order to decide who his
allies should be.

His childhood friends, Perdiccas and Hephaistion,
accompanied by an Indian prince, went up to the
mountain villages to consolidate Alexander's rule.
With the rest of his army, he himself proceeded to
the valleys which lay in the shadow of the
Himalayas.

There were violent clashes. Here in India, battle
techniques were different, for all the various tribes
were independent, unlike the tribes under Persian
rule. Alexander's men were not used to guerrilla
warfare and he was obliged to adopt new tactics in
order to form mobile army units.

Because of the hardships of such a long war
Alexander and his men had become very cruel.

Without the slightest hesitation, they killed and plundered and sacked whole cities.

The hardest battle of all took place at Aorno, a fine fortress. After the victory his soldiers rounded up 230,000 oxen from the area. Alexander chose the largest and healthiest of the oxen and sent them off to Macedonia to plough the fields there.

Here too as he did before, following each victory and before marching on, he left garrisons to watch

over each post. But in this area they did not last long. As soon as Alexander was out of sight, the princes of India attacked and overthrew them.

One of Alexander's main enemies was the Indian king Poros, who rejected the Macedonian's sovereignty and refused to pay taxes. He also denied the conqueror's right to come anywhere near the boundaries of his kingdom. Nevertheless Alexander dispatched 6000 foot-soldiers and 5000 cavalry to the River Jhelum. In the middle of the night, they crossed the river to confront Poros and his soldiers, along with 200 elephants and 300 chariots.
But the chariots got stuck in the muddy river and were useless. The elephants, though, trampled many Greek foot-soldiers to death. King Poros' generals and his two sons were killed. He himself was wounded and had no choice but to surrender. Alexander let the Indian king keep his title and kingdom, because he was well aware that he didn't have enough men to control the newly-won territories.
By way of exchange, Poros gave Alexander 5000 Indian soldiers and lots of elephants to continue his march to the Orient.

In succession, the cities of India fell, in the wake of Alexander's mighty power. His aim now was to reach the River Ganges, where he expected to come face to face with the next strong kingdom of India. But his army had reached the end of their endurance. His soldiers were exhausted. Eight long years had gone by since the start of the expedition. The men longed to return home, so they rebelled. Up until now, Alexander had been able to convince them to carry on with him. Not any longer. An old soldier stood up and reminded him of all the men who had been killed or had died as a result of sickness and hardships or had been forced to remain in garrisons in distant lands with hardly any hope of ever returning to their homeland. Only 334 men were still left out of the thousands and thousands who had set out from Macedonia eight years ago. That night Alexander spent wide awake in his tent. He needed to reflect and make up his mind.

Next day he came out and in public admitted this was the end of the expedition to the Orient.

He told them to get ready for the journey back home. Twelve tall altars were built along the banks of the Hyphasi River to mark the end of Alexander's conquests.

On his way back, he halted twice in order to found two more cities. One of them he called Nicaea from the Greek word for victory, and the other Bucephalus for his favourite horse which had died of old age.

In the winter of 325 B.C. he reached Patala near the mouth of the Indus River in India. Here, Alexander decided to divide his army into three sections.

One section, along with the elephants, would go back the way they had come, led by Crateros.

The second section, under the leadership of Nearchus, was sent on by ship. As for the third section, Alexander chose the route along the seacoast in order to prepare and provide his fleet with food and water in all the various ports.

Now the young Macedonian and his men set out on their way back. They had to cross the vast Baluchistan Desert. Thousands of his men died of hunger and thirst. Only when they reached Pura, were they able to rest and recover for a brief interval.

In Carmania Alexander built another city named after himself. He organised sacrifices to the gods, as well as games, parades, symposia and other festivities which lasted seven whole days.

Then he went back to Persepolis and Susa. Upon his return, he discovered that the rulers he had appointed there had been unjust and corrupt. They had overtaxed the people and kept all the money for themselves. They thought Alexander had been lost in India and would never return to check up on them. But now that he had returned, their punishment was severe.

In Susa, in accordance with Persian custom, he married two princesses, both of whom were descendants of Darius. On the same day, a ceremony took place where many of his officers married Persian girls from good families. Alexander considered these marriages a political act of alliance and a proof of the continued cooperation between Macedonians and Persians. His companions disagreed with his actions. They resented his orders to learn the language of strange foreigners and to dress up in odd clothes.
They resented it when he bestowed Greek military titles on Persians. Soldiers who had been faithful to him up until now realised that soon enough, strangers would replace them in his affections.

Alexander's new plan now was to sail round Arabia. Then – with Egypt as his base – he planned to move on to conquer Carthage and Rome. Apparently there was to be no return for him.

Unexpectedly his best friend, Hephaistion, died in
Ecbatana. Alexander went there for the funeral.
He was extremely sad, but had no time for
mourning. There was too much to be done.
He had to give orders for the next campaign.
He also was obliged to welcome foreign dignitaries
who kept pouring in from every corner of the
world and also had to play the role of judge
and take part in various revels.

On one such occasion, after a long bout of
drinking, Alexander decided to take a swim in
order to sober up. But instead, he became very ill.
Each passing day he got worse and worse, until he
was actually burning with fever. In agony, his best
friends stood near him, hoping against hope that
he would get better.
But he himself realised that he was about to die.
"I leave my kingdom to the best man," he said.
Four days later he passed away.

The entire kingdom mourned him deeply.
A splendid chariot was constructed to carry
Alexander's body back to his birthplace in
Macedonia.
But the fight over succession had already begun.
One of his closest companions, Ptolemy, stole his
body, took it to Egypt and buried it somewhere in
Alexandria. By so doing, Ptolemy hoped to be
considered the rightful heir to the empire.

Alexander never returned to his motherland.
But he lived on in the legends and tales of all the
peoples he conquered. He was portrayed in
different ways, sometimes as an ancient Greek,
sometimes as a Persian, sometimes as an Indian
or Egyptian. Precisely as he wanted to be:
constantly changing forms according to the
different civilisations he came to know as a traveller.
Perhaps the most authentic portrayal of Alexander
the Great is as the Ruler of the World crowned
with the moon and the sun symbol of Vergina.

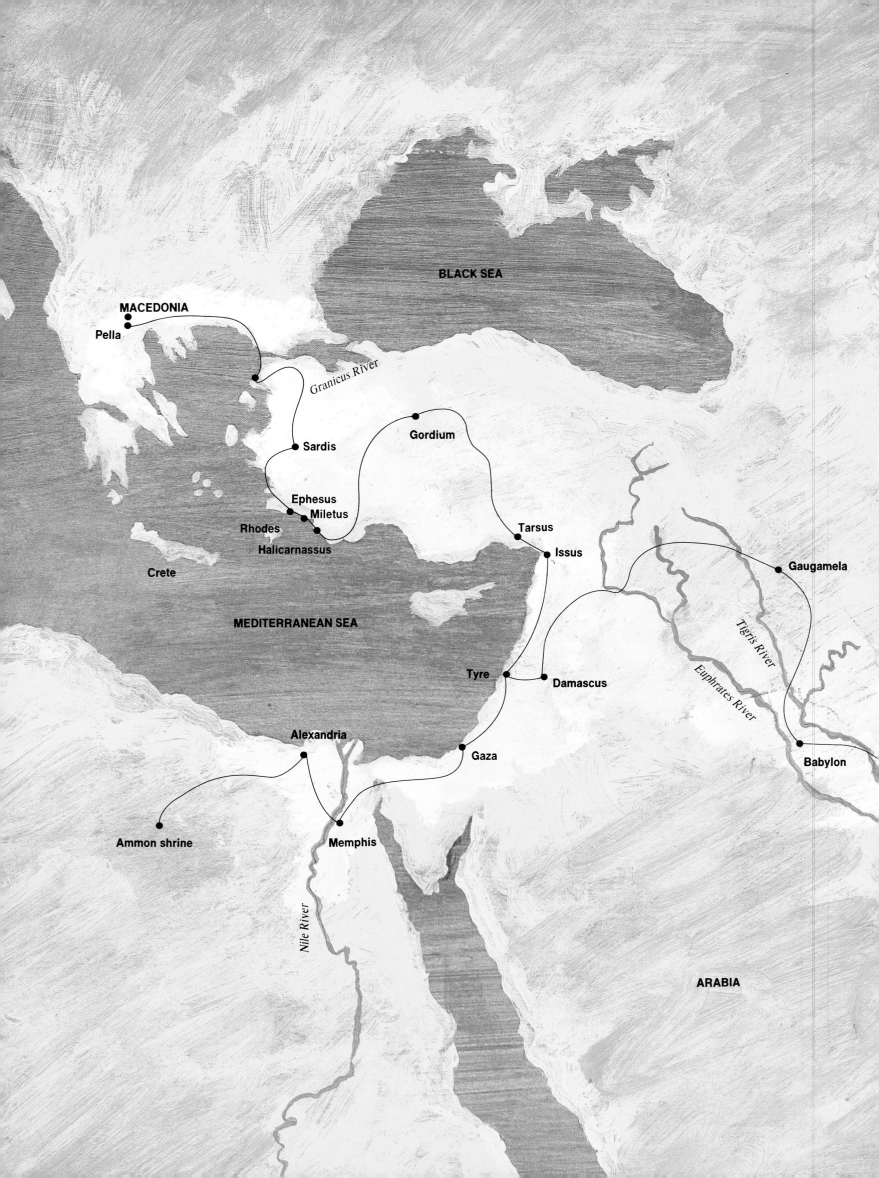

BLACK SEA

MACEDONIA
Pella

Granicus River

Sardis

Gordium

Ephesus
Miletus
Rhodes
Halicarnassus

Tarsus

Issus

Gaugamela

Crete

Tigris River

MEDITERRANEAN SEA

Euphrates River

Tyre

Damascus

Babylon

Alexandria

Gaza

Ammon shrine

Memphis

Nile River

ARABIA

CASPIAN
SEA

SOGDIANA

HYRCANIA

BACTRIANA

Taxila

Bactra

Ecbatana

Alexandria Areion

Bucephala

Nicaea

Hydaspes River

Susa

ARACHOSIA

Alexandria of Arachosia

DRANGIANA

Hyphasis River

Pasargadae

Indus River

Persepolis

CARMANIA

Harmozia

GEDROSIA

PERSIAN
GULF

Patala

OTHER BOOKS BY SOFIA ZARABOUKA:

 1. IN THE FOREST
 2. THE DIRTY VILLAGE
 3. THE STORY OF MY MOTHER

 4. FLIT GOES ON A TRIP
 5. FLIT GOES FISHING
 6. FLIT GOES ON A CRUISE
 7. FLIT GOES TO SCHOOL
 8. FLY-FLY
 9. MRS. ANNOULA
10. THE CIRCUS
11. PEACE

ADAPTED FOR CHILDREN:
12. ARISTOPHANES' THE BIRDS
13. ARISTOPHANES' PEACE
14. ARISTOPHANES' LYSISTRATA
15. ARISTOPHANES' PLUTUS
16. ARISTOPHANES' THE FROGS
17. MYTHOLOGY 1: THE CREATION OF THE WORLD. TITANS. ZEUS AND HIS FAMILY
18. MYTHOLOGY 2: HERA, HEPHAESTUS, APHRODITE AND ARES
19. MYTHOLOGY 3: ATHENE, POSEIDON, APOLLO AND ARTEMIS
20. MYTHOLOGY 4: HERMES, PLUTO, PERSEPHONE, DEMETER AND DIONYSUS
21. MYTHOLOGY 5: THE FATES, PROMETHEUS, PANDORA, DEUCALION AND THE WINDS
22. MYTHOLOGY 6: EOS, HELIUS, PHAETHON, SELENE AND PAN
23. MYTHOLOGY 7: THE CENTAURS, ASCLEPIUS, THE MUSES AND ORPHEUS
24. MYTHOLOGY 8: EUROPE AND CADMUS, TANTALUS AND PELOPS, DANAUS, PERSEUS AND MEDUSA
25. MYTHOLOGY 9: HERACLES
26. MYTHOLOGY 10: THESEUS

27. THE A B C's
28. LITTLE RED RIDING HOOD
29. THE THREE LITTLE PIGS
30. MIAOW
31. A LITTLE TINY BIT
32. THE KING'S APPLE TREE
33. ODYSSEY
34. ILIAD
35. THE ATOMS EASY FOR A CAT
36. PLAYS FOR CHILDREN
37. THE SAGA OF ALEXANDER THE GREAT

Typeset in Greece
by Photokyttaro Ltd.
14, Armodiou St., Athens 105 52, Tel. 32.44.111
Printed by
A. & P. Spyrou
Vyronos 9, Dafni, Tel. 97.51.207
For Kedros Publishers, S.A.,
3, G. Gennadiou St., Athens 106 78,
Tel. 38.09.712 – Fax 38.31.981
Jule 1997